OUT OF THE TOP DRAWER

Out of the the Top Drawer

Stories to tell again

CYRIL DAVEY

London EPWORTH PRESS

Printed in Great Britain
by Billing & Sons Limited
Guildford and London

SBN 7162 0157 7

Preface

Between 1950 and 1965 I contributed several series of children's stories to the *British Weekly* and the *Sunday School Chronicle*, as well as a daily feature to the *Liverpool Evening Post*. In addition, I was a frequent contributor to the BBC's *Five to Ten* feature. All the material, as well as a good deal which was never used, was kept in the top drawer of my filing cabinet. Other duties, claiming so much time that little is left for writing, have brought this particular 'piece of writing' to an end. So have changing patterns in journals and the BBC, as well as the demise of the Liverpool newspaper!

One evening, recently, I decided to clear away some of the years' accumulation. It seemed a pity to throw everything away when people still tell me they are glad of material, not only for children's talks (now all much shorter than they used to be) but for adult occasions as well. Instead of discarding everything I put some back – who doesn't do the same? But, for the sake of those who can use it, I am glad to share, from sources ancient and modern, true and fabled, acknowledged and often unacknowledged, some of the things that came *Out of the Top Drawer*.

CYRIL DAVEY

Contents

(2) For Older People

(1) For Boys and Girls

Importance

One Sunday afternoon the Primary Department Leader was talking about all the wonderful things that had happened in the world since she herself was a little girl. High-speed aircraft crossing the Atlantic . . . space-craft high above the earth . . . colour television . . . it was really quite a long list.

The next Sunday afternoon she started by asking them if they remembered what she had been talking about. They nodded their heads wisely, and said 'Yes, miss' in tiny, sharp voices.

'Good,' she said. 'We were talking about all the wonderful things that have happened in the world we live in. Now . . . can you tell me one very important thing that wasn't in the world when *I* was a little girl?'

Jane had no hesitation at all. 'Yes, miss. *Me*, miss!'

Napier

A few generations ago everyone would have known his name. Now very few people who look at his statue know anything about him at all. It is a pity, for Sir Charles Napier was not only a great general, but a fine and generous man, too. He first made his reputation in the war against Napoleon. Then he joined the Greeks in their fight against the Turks who were invading their country and almost became their commander-in-chief. Later still, in the middle of the century, he conquered much of North India and added it to the British Empire.

We do not think as much of soldiers, even generals, as we used to do, and it is not by warfare that men can be judged today. There are other reasons for counting Napier a great man, however, and one story will show what sort of man he really was.

One day he was walking home over the moors of northern England when he came across a small boy crying by the side of the road. At his feet lay the remains of a broken basin. He had been sent to take his father's dinner to work and had dropped the basin on the way home. The general was employed, in those days, in keeping many of the rough north-country workmen in order, and he told the boy sharply to stop crying at once. He looked up, more than a little frightened.

'I'll give you sixpence to buy a new basin. Don't worry.'

To a poor family sixpence was a lot of money, and basins were not easily bought. But when the general put his hand in his pocket he found he had no money. He had left his purse at home.

'Be here tomorrow morning at this time and I will give you the sixpence.'

When he reached home he found a letter from a friend asking him to meet him the following day. They had not seen each other for a long time, and might not meet again for years. (We would not know the story unless we had the letter which Napier wrote – and unless the boy had told it many times.)

'I am so sorry', the general wrote to his friend, 'but I have already made an appointment for tomorrow – and I cannot break it.'

The Ragged Ruler

Mahmud of Ghazni was one of the best-known and most-feared conquerors of the Middle Ages in Asia. He kept his throne by force and terror. Yet, in his own way, he could be generous, too.

There was his servant, Ayaz, for instance.

Ayaz, a poor man, had once been a common-place servant but, for some reason, he came to the Emperor's notice. Mahmud found him honest and hard-working, and promoted him. Again and again he was advanced, until at last he was put in charge of the Emperor's treasure. It was then that jealous men began to talk and spread scandalous stories in the hope that they would lead to Ayaz's downfall. Ayaz, they said, was stealing the Emperor's treasures little by little.

If he was not doing so, they asked smoothly, why did he spend half an hour each day in the treasury, always making sure that he was alone.

It was the Emperor Mahmud himself who solved the mystery. He hid in his own treasury until Ayaz came in, carrying a lamp. The servant went to a small box, unlocked it, drew out a bundle of old ragged clothes and dressed himself in them instead of his own rich garments. Then, in the clothes he used to wear, he knelt down, thanked Allah for his good fortune, and prayed that he might be kept honest and faithful.

Getting Prayer Answered

Two stories illustrate one fact about prayer, and show why some people say God does not answer them when they pray.

The first comes from India, that land of barren plains and rainless months. A missionary once found a group of tired, anxious villagers who had gone day after day to the shrine outside the village, laying rice-cakes before the weather-beaten statue of the god. It was no use preaching to them that Jesus was 'the water of life' when their tank was empty and the skies had no clouds. And when they urged him to pray to his own god for rain he simply walked round the village, looking here and there, measuring, calculating, examining the lie of the land. Then, at last, he promised to pray if they would join him. The promise came very quickly. Even prayer to a strange god was better than no water. But they were shocked at his next words

'Go and get some spades. If you pray with me you will need them!'

In groups of three or four the men began to dig where the stranger pointed, and he dug alongside them. After all, he had promised to pray, too.

Down went the hole, while the men changed shifts throughout the day. Deeper went the hole the next day, and the day after, though the villagers were growing angry and sceptical. This was no way to pray, they grumbled. Indeed, they had almost given up when one of them shouted that the ground seemed to be getting damp. Another six feet, and water was seeping into the hole. With new excitement other men waited to take their turn until at last the well was dug.

'It's no use praying unless you are prepared to work as well,' said the stranger, Now, at last, they could understand that Jesus really was the water of life.

The second story comes from the other side of the Atlantic, and was first told by the great American preacher, Dr Fosdick. There was once a boat caught in a storm, he said – a storm so bad the sails were furled so that they should not be torn, and the engine failed as the water beat down into the cabin and engine-room. Tossed about by the huge waves, the little crew were sick, worn out and almost hopeless. The only thing seemed to be to wait until the storm blew itself out – and yet, if they did so, the little boat might be beaten to pieces. Suddenly one of the crew had a strange feeling. His mother would know of their plight. At this moment she would be praying for their safety. Things would work out right after all. He shouted to his friends, new hope in his voice.

'My mother will be praying for us at this very moment.' They stared at his excited face. 'Let's get to work. We've got to get her prayer answered!'

Eight Days of Courage

Deoghar lies on the main railway-line from Calcutta to North-west India. One night, in 1950, there was a dreadful accident there. The Punjab Mail, travelling at full speed, was derailed and plunged down a steep embankment. It lay, a smoking, fiery ruin in the darkness, and hundreds of passengers were killed or injured. Before long, scores of them began to make their way, some carrying friends or family, to the little, overworked, under-staffed hospital at Deoghar.

It was early on Sunday morning that the news reached St Mary's School, and at once a deputation of senior Guides and other Christian girls went to the Principal asking permission for some of the best-qualified Guides to help in the hospital.

'But it's only a day or so to your school-leaving examinations', the Principal reminded them.

That did not matter as much as helping where help was needed. For the next eight days the Guides worked in three-hour shifts, sharing the dreadful toil of the hospital. When it was over the doctor said it would have been impossible to carry on without their help.

During those eight days, while they were working both day and night, the girls sat for their annual, and some of them for the end-of-school, examinations. And passed.

The Bishop and the Brass Plate

Cecil Hunt was a 'literary agent' – that is, a man who receives books and stories from authors and tries to 'place' them with publishers and papers. Some of them were very good. Some of them *might* have been very good if . . . The 'if' was a big one. Writers who were just beginning their careers never seemed to think it mattered if they rubbed words out and wrote them in again in pencil . . . or if they got their spelling wrong . . . or if they did not put the commas and semicolons in the right places.

To people like this Mr Hunt sometimes told the story of the bishop who found the choirboy polishing the great brass plate which stood on the altar. It shone like gold, and the boy stood back admiring it, while the bishop smiled approvingly. Then the bishop picked it up – and turned it over. The choirboy began to shuffle. He looked the other way when the bishop looked at him.

'If you want to please the angels, my lad', he said, 'you'd better try polishing the back as well as the front!'

Twentieth-century Redskin

'That's where they were murdered.'

The visitor looked at the little log-cabin, nestling peacefully in the valley. He had crossed the Atlantic for the first time and had taken time off to visit the Red Indian country. A friendly man whom he had met had offered to show him round.

'The Indians came out of the woods, just there. Led by their chief, they came to take vengeance on the white men. They had no reason to love them, and they massacred every man, woman and child in the place, just where they were camping for the night by the cabin they were building.'

He paused while the visitor looked down into the valley.

'But times have changed. I suppose you're surprised to see an Indian dressed just the same as you are.'

'Well, I didn't really expect to find Red Indians wearing war-paint and feathers.'

'Some do, you know . . . for the sake of the tourists. And it isn't really so long ago since most of them did, when they were on the war-path like the men who killed those settlers. Did you expect to find them living in towns, driving automobiles, running department stores?'

'I hadn't thought much about it. Perhaps not. Times *have* changed, haven't they?'

'Very much so', said the friendly guide. 'I am a minister, with a church there in the town'.

He led his guest up the path from the log-cabin.

'But the chief who killed those white settlers was my great-grandfather.'

The Four Wallendas

The Four Wallendas were one of the most famous high-wire acts in circus history. Everyone who remembers Bertram Mills's Circus a few years ago will recall how the audience held its breath while they performed their act. Two men walking the high-wire with a pole between them, on their shoulders . . . a chair balanced on the pole . . . another man sitting in the chair . . . and, on the shoulders of the man on the chair on the pole on the two men on the wire, a girl was balanced.

It was in Glasgow that disaster overtook them. It had nothing to do with the quality of their act, and it was certainly not their fault. The supports of their platform gave away and the Wallendas crashed to the ground. Lulu was carried to hospital with a twisted back. Willi had a badly damaged wrist.

The next night a disappointed audience, grateful, however, they were not there when the accident happened, came to the circus knowing they would have to miss the top act of the show. To their amazement the three remaining Wallendas came into the ring and began to climb towards the wire, though Lulu was still in hospital.

Previously Willi had sat on the chair while Lulu stood on his shoulders. Now, however, while the chair was balanced on the pole carried by the two unhurt performers Willi swung himself up on to the chair –

but instead of sitting on it he twisted feet uppermost, balancing himself on his injured wrist. Sweat dropped from his forehead to the sawdust, but he finished the act before he came down.

'I had to prove something to myself,' he said, grimly, when the reporters asked him about it afterwards. 'If I had not gone up tonight I would never have dared to go on the wire again.

'You see . . . I was afraid of being afraid.'

The Saint Who Gave Away

There was once a poor Spanish boy who got into dreadful trouble from his father because he gave the family's six chickens to six poor beggars at the door. Many years later he lay dying. By that time he had achieved great things and become Archbishop of Valencia. He waved his thin hand and a servant came at once.

'I have five thousand ducats in my treasury,' he whispered. 'Give it to the poor. Tell me when it is done.'

A few hours later the treasurer came to him, telling him that the money had been given away. But in his hand he held a little bag. A man who owed some money to the Archbishop wanted to pay his debt while he had time.

'It's midnight,' said the dying man. 'I cannot keep this money now. What good will it do me? Give it away, as you did the rest.'

'I am happy to die a poor friar,' he murmured when he heard that it had been done. Then he turned to one of the palace servants. 'I have nothing left now . . . only this bed I lie on. I give it to you. It is no longer mine. I want to go to God just as I came from him – with nothing.'

No wonder that when he died they called him Saint Thomas! But a greater tribute still was the inscription on his tomb. It contained only his name – and the two words: 'He Gave.'

The Gentle Slave

Pierre Toussaint was a Haitian, a slave in a French family which had escaped during a revolution in the island. Treated far more gently than most slaves, Pierre was much more a friend of the family than a servant, and with very good reason. When Monsieur Berard, his master, died it was he who cared for his mistress in their new life in America as he had done for the whole family in Haiti.

The island had been part of the French Empire until the French Revolution broke out, and then the Negroes in the West Indian island had risen in revolt against their masters, killing, imprisoning or driving them out so that they could set up a new 'black republic'. Now, Toussaint was in New York, and had learned to be a barber and hairdresser. There were few of the great French houses, or English-speaking ones, either, where he was not known. Given his freedom in Madame Berard's will, he was able to run his own business. His customers were well pleased with his skill, and often paid more than they were asked.

Pierre Toussaint never said no to the 'tip', however large. He smiled, bowed, and put it in his pouch. But that was not all. Whatever he received, either in payment or 'tips', went down in his neat handwriting in the little pocket book he carried with him. These entries went on the side headed 'Receipts'. On the other side there were only initials, one on each line. Pierre alone knew what they stood for. Sometimes they would have meant nothing to anybody, except himself, for he was very careful what he wrote. But every entry was followed by a figure – the money he gave away.

The letters which came to Pierre can still be seen and read . . . from the sick, the poor, the prisoners, the emigrants from France in the days of the Revolution, the people who had escaped from Haiti, the orphans – letters which asked for help, or said a word of thanks for it when they had received it. Pierre never forgot what it had been like to be a slave, poor, without money, always dependent on other people. He very seldom said 'no'. He would rather ask one of his wealthy patrons for a larger tip than usual!

One day, when he was very old, a customer looked at his white head, shrivelled black skin and bent back. 'Why don't you give up working, Pierre?' he asked. 'Surely you've gone on long enough?'

Pierre Toussaint smiled gently. 'If I gave up working, how would I be able to help anyone – without begging myself?'

Wet Paint!

She was about seven, and she walked daintily down the road on her way to school. She wore a clean dress, and her fair pony-tail was tied back with blue ribbon. She was in no hurry to get to school. First, she stopped to pat a brown-and-white dog. Then she ran across the road to say 'Hello' to the postman on the other pavement. Finally, she reached the bottom of the road. It was just there that she smelt the smell.

It was fresh, clean and inviting – just like the smell her daddy had made when he was repainting the kitchen the week before. On the bright green railings a notice was hanging, and Sarah went very close to spell it out.

'Wet . . . paint.' Someone had thoughtfully hung the warning on the railings.

Sarah wrinkled her nose. You could almost see the question in her mind. She put out her hand – one little finger first, and then her whole hand round the bright green railing. Would it be wet?

It was!

Sarah wiped her hand down her clean blue dress and went on her way to school.

The Emerald Vase

In the cathedral at Genoa is an emerald vase – very old, undoubtedly, but surely not so old as tradition claims. It is said by the guides that it belonged to King Solomon. Indeed, they will tell you that it was one of the gifts which was presented to him by the Queen of Sheba.

Solomon, so the story goes, used the vase to store a special liquid of which he alone knew the secret. It was the 'elixir of life'. It was so powerful that the tiniest sip of it could prolong someone's life for years. Naturally sooner or later, everyone came to know of the wonderful gift which the Queen of Sheba had brought. With a small sip at a time King Solomon could live for ever!

Other people wanted life, too. On one occasion a criminal in prison dared to ask for a sip. What the king said about *him* can easily be imagined. He was going to save it for people more worthy of it. Then it was a woman whose son was dying. 'If she had been a widow . . .' said the king. But, after all, she had a husband to look after her. Yet when a widow did come and plead for a single sip he found a good reason for sending her away, too.

'I will only give it where it is really deserved,' he stated.

Somehow, no one ever seemed to deserve even a sip of the wonderful liquid and, in time, people forgot all about it or else came to believe it had never existed at all. Then came the day when the king, tired and old, lay dying. This was the moment when the elixir of life could really prove its value. The emerald vase was brought from the treasure chamber – brought with state and opened with ceremony. But it was too late.

The king who had refused his mercy to so many, good and bad, found that the bottle was empty. It had evaporated because he had kept it to himself.

Perfection

Michelangelo, the greatest sculptor of his age, has left plenty of work behind him. Almost all of it looks perfect.

It is said that a friend once came to visit his studio after not seeing him for some time. He looked round in surprise. The statues were still in the same places, and they still looked much the same. 'Haven't you been doing any work on these?' he asked.

'I have reshaped that hand . . . altered the line of those lips . . . softened the way that robe falls to the floor.'

'Why, yes,' said his friend. 'I can see that now. But these things are only trifles.'

Michelangelo answered quietly. 'Indeed they are. But trifles make perfection – and perfection is no trifle!'

Eiffel Tower

Who built the Eiffel Tower?

Every summer thousands of school-children stand and gaze up at it. A million visitors a year glide upwards in the lift and look down on Paris from the top, a thousand feet above the city. But who built it?

Gustave Eiffel not only built the tower that bears his name. He was a pioneer in every form of engineering. His bridges, the first to be made of 'prefabricated steel' instead of wood and stone, were put up in half the time of the old ones, and cost only half as much. The French ones were followed by bridges in Russia, Egypt, Peru and all over Europe.

He built dams, factories, stations – all at a price that left his competitors gasping. When the sculptor Bartholdi was creating the Statue of Liberty for the United States, to symbolize Franco-American friendship, he showed him how it could be created and held safely against the winds and tides of the Atlantic.

In 1889 the Eiffel Tower was completed, and for three-quarters of a century did not need the replacement of a single girder or rivet.

Eiffel had two mottoes. The first was: 'If you've got a job to do you may as well enjoy it.'

The other he put very plainly, too. 'Whatever I have, and whatever I do or invent, I want as many people as possible to share.'

Castle of Fear

Caesar Augustus gave his name to many places throughout the Roman Empire, though we remember him best because one of the summer months, August, is named after him. Some of the places which bear his name have so altered with the years that the name is now hard to recognize. One of these is Saragossa, in Spain, a corruption of 'Caesar Augusta'.

The people of Saragossa still tell a strange legend. Not far from the town, in the mountains, they say, is 'Fear Castle'. 'The Lord of Fear Castle' is a terrible spirit indeed. Whatever evil befell the neighbourhood was attributed to him. Summers too wet or too dry were his doing, and if plague struck the town it was because the Lord of Fear Castle was angry or just plain spiteful. A peasant would cross himself if you asked the way to the strange castle, and hurry away without answering. If you pressed them they would agree that it was true – there was such a place, away in the mountains, hard of approach. Only a few people had ever got near it.

The brave men who tried to find it, however, had a stranger story still.

'It is there, truly enough. You can see it from a distance, nearly blocking the valley. Thunder rolls as you go up the valley. Nothing could look more solid. It is so frightening that the only sensible thing seems to be to run away. And yet – the moment you reach its walls, the whole thing disappears.'

The Black Man

Few people who saw the chubby, cheerful little black

boy running amongst the huts of the African village where he grew up would ever have imagined he would grow up to be the Vice-Principal of Achimota College, later to be part of the University of Ghana.

In the same way, few people who met him on his travels knew him for what he was. In America, and even in Britain, he was elbowed off pavements, or off tram-cars and buses. He was too great a man to be bitter, though he was often hurt.

On one occasion he was returning to Africa by sea. The steward in the dining saloon set a table for two, but when his fellow-traveller saw that he was to eat with a Negro he demanded that the steward find him another table. The African sat alone throughout the voyage. It was on that same ship that another traveller put a question to him.

'If you could come back into the world again, what would you like to be?'

Kwegyir Aggrey, the great Negro leader, answered very quickly and surely. 'If I were coming back into the world again I would go to God and say: "Send me back black – as black as you can make me. I have a work to do for my people that no white man can do!"'

Where King David Slept

There is a very old folk-tale from Palestine about King David's tomb. It is said to be near Jerusalem – some-where, but no one knows quite where.

The story tells how two Jewish boys, in the days of long ago, once lost a lamb from their flock. In searching for it, they stumbled on the entrance to a cave they had never seen before and could never again find after-wards. They crept through the entrance, excited at the thought of hidden treasure, quite forgetting their search for the lost lamb.

Once inside, they found themselves in a huge, vaulted chamber where, amongst ancient armour, jewels and gold, slept King David, the greatest ruler of the Jewish people. The King stirred and, turning over, pointed to the gold and precious stones. Both boys scooped up a handful and then, turning and scrambling upwards, they found their way out of the cave. Scared almost out of their lives, they reached the open air and looked at the riches in their hands. As they stared, the gold changed to red dust in their palms and, when they turned round, they saw the entrance to the cave disappearing into the face of the rocks. But a voice seemed to echo in the hills.

'You forgot the lamb. There is no treasure for those who forget their duty.'

The Wooden Bell

The magistrate looked very sternly at the Burmese peasant who stood before him. It was in the days before the country became independent, and the magistrate was a British officer. 'Is it true that you stole this bell?' he asked.

The villager nodded.

It was a wooden bell, roughly made, with two wood clappers inside. Such bells were widely used in the Shan States and on the borders of India and China, and were fastened to the necks of cows which fed on the hillsides – very much like Swiss or Austrian cowbells today. The thief was a simple villager, with a cow or two of his own. For some reason he had stolen a bell from a neighbour's cow and fastened it round his own animal's neck.

'I shall fine you five rupees', said the magistrate.

'*Five rupees!*' stammered the poor man. 'But that is the fine for stealing a *copper* bell, like I could buy in the market in the town.'

The officer nodded. 'That is so. If you had stolen a copper bell I would have fined you only half that much. This wooden bell you didn't need to steal at all. You could have made one of your own, as easily as that man made his. Instead, you stole one from a man who had gone to the trouble of making it.'

He shook his head sadly.

'Five rupees is the fine – for being lazy as well as being a thief.'

The Boy and the Lawn-mower

Dr Harry Emerson Fosdick, the great American preacher, made everyone listen when he preached and, when he wrote, people all over the world read his books. He made it look easy, too. People would say: 'I wonder why I can't do that?' – as though preaching or writing were some special trick he had learned. 'What is the secret?' they asked.

Dr Fosdick once explained the secret – and went on to say that there were many times when he did *not* want to preach, or write, or study, or do all the things that had to be done if he was to be as perfect as he could be. 'But,' he said, 'I always remember my father.

'When he was going out one morning, my father stopped at the door and said something to my mother.

I heard him. "This lawn needs cutting. Harry can cut it if he likes!" '

At the gate he turned round, and shouted something else.

'He'd better like, too!'

The Inventor and the Eggs

It was a queer sight – a little boy, five years old, sitting carefully on a nest of duck's eggs, trying to hatch them.

He was born in 1847, in Ohio, and everywhere in the world people are in debt to him. Watch television . . . listen to the radio or a gramophone . . . send a telegram – all these things we owe partly to him. Type a letter . . . go to the cinema – it's the same thing. Switch on an electric light – and you have the benefit of hundreds of experiments he carried out, almost all of them failures, until at last he succeeded in doing what he *knew* could be done.

His name was Thomas Alva Edison.

It all goes back to that barn in Ohio. One day he disappeared and it was only after a long search that his mother and father found him in a neighbour's barn, sitting on the duck's eggs which the duck had deserted. They picked him up and carried him home, worried and cross about his stupid prank.

The next day he was missing again. This time they went straight to the barn, and there was Thomas, sitting on the eggs. Now his father was very angry indeed, and Thomas went home under his arm. But all the way his shrill little voice yelled the same thing.

' 'I *can* hatch 'em! I *know* I can hatch 'em if I sit there long enough!'

The Robber Indian

Buster Whiteway was a half-caste Red Indian accused of robbery with violence. For a long time the police had been searching for him but it was the famous Canadian Mounted Police who caught up with him in his hiding place. One of the 'Mounties', Corporal Graves, was detailed to take Buster back to stand trial and, with two other passengers, they set off in a small aircraft towards 'civilisation'.

It was over Moose Lake that a violent storm struck the plane, which lost a wing and came hurtling down to the ice-bound surface of the lake. Spence, the pilot, was flung from the machine and killed. Buster was thrown through a door and lay unconscious with a broken ankle. The policeman and the other two passengers were badly injured and unconscious.

Slowly Buster came to his senses. With great pain he dragged the three men into the shadow of the aircraft, crawled in and out to get eiderdowns and rugs, and wrapped the men in them. But even with one ankle broken he was able to get away. He set across the frozen lake – a free man again. The temperature was below zero as he dragged himself away.

Hours later, after collapsing a dozen times, the half-breed robber stumbled into an Indian settlement, just in time to send a group of rescuers to save the lives of his companions.

The Gift of Grapes

Macarius, so the legends say, was so gentle that he even changed the lives of the monks who came to live with him. That may sound odd, but not even all monks were saints.

Macarius himself, a kind and gracious man, was a hermit, with a cell in the desert, and his reputation was so great that others came to listen to him and, in time, many of them chose to live near him, making their own cells and homes in the holes and caves of the rocks. His lonely sanctuary became a colony. Not all who came, however, were anything like Macarius. Some were selfish, some were critical of other monks who lived there, others complained bitterly about the way people sought out Macarius for help and advice instead of seeking them. None of them lived near Macarius for long, however, before something happened to them.

One day a visitor brought the gentle monk a bunch of luscious grapes. The old man looked at them, thanked the giver for his generosity, and laid them aside. They were far too good for him, he thought. Waiting until it was dark, he slipped out of his cell, and put them just inside the cell of a neighbouring hermit. Then, very late at night, there was a footstep inside his own cell and he looked up to see a middle-aged man, who, on his arrival, had been one of the worst-tempered and selfish of all of them. In his hands he held the bunch of grapes.

'These are for you, father', he said, and went quietly out into the night.

The old man sighed gently, and thanked God. He knew what had happened. Each man had passed them on, quietly and generously, to his neighbour until the grapes had gone full circle, ending where they began.

The Circus is Here!

The first circus in the world was begun by Sergeant-Major Philip Astley when he left the 15th Royal

Regiment of Light Dragoons. The 'Seven Years War' was over when he retired from the Army in 1763, and he was given a white charger by his colonel, in recognition of his courage and gallantry. Not sure how to make a living, the sergeant-major began to give displays. It was the beginning of 'the greatest show on earth'.

Then, at the horse-market at Smithfield – which used to be the 'smooth field' and was the district where tournaments were held in the middle ages – he bought a little pony for £5, and taught it to do tricks. Soon he was billing it as 'The Little Learned Military Horse'. He announced that it would 'lie dead in a manner most extraordinary' and 'fire a pistol at a word of command and do upwards of five hundred feats'. When he decided to advertise his 'circus', Billy, the Military Horse, was the star figure, for he rode in a carriage, sitting on a seat with a clown by his side.

But Philip Astley was more than a showman, a sort of Barnum and Bailey figure a hundred years before the great circus names. When he rejoined the Army in 1792 to fight for the British against Napoleon, he took with him an extra flannel waistcoat for every man with whom he served. They were very welcome, too, in the cold winter days of the Continental campaigns. Every waistcoat had been made by the ladies of his circus, and inside each was sewn a shilling – a lot of money in those days. He called it 'the soldiers' friend in need', and there were times, when men were wounded or stranded, when the shilling really did become a friend.

Nobody has suggested that Sergeant-Major Astley was a very religious man – but he knew a good deal about giving pleasure and help to very ordinary people.

Four of a Kind

There is always somebody who has never heard the story of the four beggars, old though it is.

They met outside the city gate, after they had begged their way through the city – so the Eastern storytellers say. It was a hot day, and they were not very good at begging. Or perhaps they looked so rascally that no one would give them much. Anyway they met by accident and carefully showed each other what they had gained. One had a few handfuls of rice. The second some vegetables. The third had a little meat, and the fourth some spices.

'The rice would be better with spices,' grumbled the first man.

'Vegetables would make my meat a lot more tasty,' said the third.

Then, with the same idea in all their minds, they looked at each other. They nodded. 'Let's put it together and make a good curry-stew.'

As the darkness fell they fetched water from the well and set it to boil over a fire of twigs collected from the trees by the gate. By the time it was boiling darkness had fallen. 'In with your rice,' said the man with the meat. The first beggar put his hand into the pot. 'Now the vegetables,' he said to his neighbour. Each man put his hand into the pot, and they sat waiting for it to heat up into a tasty stew. The smell was not very noticeable but, after a while, they placed their dishes on the ground and began to pour out the stew.

But something odd had happened. There was no stew. Only boiling water. No rice, no spices, no vegetables, no meat.

Each of the beggars had had the same idea.

Look – No Hands!

Little Andrew had been reading quietly on the hearth-rug. The book had been a Christmas present, put aside for a while, but now he had started to read he could not put it down, even to go for his tea. It was full of stories of heroes of many lands and many ages. There was the story of Schweitzer, who gave up his career to go to Africa . . . of a Scout who won a medal from the Queen because he never failed to keep the whole hospital ward cheerful, even though he had polio. There were stories of war and peace, but the one which fascinated Andrew most was about a man who had no hands.

He was a soldier who had gone out to save a comrade under fire in the war. The man was lying in a mined area and a mine exploded as his rescuer reached him. He saved his friend, but lost his hands in doing so. For ever afterwards he would have to wear artificial hands, in leather gloves.

It was three days later that Andrew came running home from school very fast. Bursting into the kitchen, he shouted: 'Mummy! I've seen him! The man with no hands!'

'You can't have done!' said his mother.

'But I *did*!' cried Andrew. 'There was an old lady coming up the hill with a huge basket of groceries from the self-service, and he walked right past her. And you know Peter Roberts . . . he was running past the man with me and he fell over. The man didn't help him at all. He had his hands in his pockets.

'He *must* be the man with no hands, mustn't he, Mummy?'

The Zebra

The four African porters had already had plenty of trouble, and now they were not only worn out but desperately hungry. Their master, who had been visiting a Government Officer many days' journey from his own home, had been attacked by a charging rhinoceros and seriously injured. Indeed, he would have been killed if the fifth porter had not stepped forward when the beast charged a second time and taken a blow from the rhino which had killed him instantly. Now, carrying the injured man, they trudged across the deserted countryside, so hungry that they would have eaten almost anything.

That was when they saw the zebra. The animal had no tail. The porters knew what that meant. In this hungry country a hunter had shot the animal and then run back to his village to tell his family that there was food for them all.

Now the porters, who had run forward as soon as they saw the zebra, stopped and stared at it. Desperately hungry, their knives were already out when they noticed the tail had gone. It was someone else's property. Shaking their heads sadly, they lifted the wounded man and trudged on again across the desert.

Black Eagle

The pioneers were gathered in their log cabin for their Sunday worship. There was much to thank God for – the new freedom they had found in America, the abundant possibilities of the place where they had planted their settlement, the quietness of Sunday after a week's hard work. The elder who was leading worship opened his Bible and began to read.

He did not notice the figures crouching by the trees. Led by Black Eagle, their chief, the Red Indians had surrounded the settlement and, as the elder prayed, Black Eagle had slipped like a shadow from the trees to the log-house. Now he stood, bent almost double, by the open window. His braves held their tomahawks loosely, waiting for the signal to attack.

Inside, the white man announced the Gospel of St Matthew, the fifth chapter. . . . 'Blessed are the poor in spirit . . . blessed are they that mourn . . . blessed are the pure in heart . . . blessed are the peace-makers . . . blessed are they that are persecuted for righteousness' sake . . .'

Swiftly Black Eagle slipped back to his startled braves. 'Leave them alone,' he ordered. 'These men are not like those I have met before. They are reading their laws. And if these are the laws by which they live we must learn from them, not kill them.'

The Stone in the Square

The land ought to have been well cultivated, bearing good crops, so the Eastern story says. Instead it was almost barren. If the peasants had worked together it could have been a place of riches, even for those who were now poor. But they refused to work with each other, to help each other, or even to work at all if they could help it. The king's town, which should have been clean, tidy and prosperous, was dirty, ill-kept and poverty-stricken. The country's leaders did nothing about it and the king himself was old, ill and almost blind.

Then, at last, the old ruler died and a new king sat on the throne in his place. Some of the thoughtful people wondered if he was going to pass laws about work, about tidying up the town and so on. He did nothing of the kind. But, within a day or two, a cart trundled out of the palace gates filled with huge stones. Going across the market-place the horse stumbled and the biggest stone of all rolled off the cart into the middle of the square. From his palace the king watched – and did nothing.

It was the same with everybody else. The carter shrugged his shoulders and went on. Stall-holders came and looked and went away. Camel-drivers urged their animals round it. It was very inconvenient, but for a week it stayed where it was. 'Why should *I* strain myself trying to move a rock like that?' each man said to himself. And so, a month after it had fallen, it was still there, a huge obstacle and a nuisance. But . . . 'It's not *my* job,' said the stall-holders, the camel-drivers, the men sitting by the roadside smoking their hookahs.

Indeed, they had something quite different to talk about. No one yet had seen the new king. Not once in the month had he come out of his palace, and the people were getting angry at his neglect. Then, one day, there was a flourish of golden trumpets. The courtiers and soldiers poured out of the gate and lined the square. The king himself came through the palace gates and walked up to the stone.

To their astonishment the great crowd of people looked as he put out one hand and slowly pushed the stone away. It was hollow! Anybody could have done it, but nobody had tried.

The king, who arranged it all, did not even make a speech. He had taught his people the lesson they needed to learn.

The Horse-shoe Nail

It was my grandmother who first told me the rhyme, so it must have been old then – so old, indeed, that I have not heard anyone repeat it for a score of years.

For the want of a nail the shoe was lost;
For the want of a shoe the horse was lost;
For the want of a horse the message was lost;
For the want of the message the battle was lost;
For the want of the battle the kingdom was lost . . .
And all for the want of one horse-shoe nail.

The Rain-maker

Kone was the rain-maker. He lived in Papua and, in his own village, he was the next most important man to the chief himself. Indeed, in some ways, he was more important. The chief could settle quarrels, declare war, demand taxes from his people – but he could not make rain.

Kone, on the other hand, was a magician, who knew the proper spells, and when the sky was cloudless and the grain was dying in the sun, villagers would come to him and ask for his help. They had to pay for it, too. If their gifts were big enough Kone would chant his spells. Sometimes, the rain came. When it failed to come, Kone explained that the gifts had not been big enough, or the gods were so angry that they would not listen.

When Chalmers, the great missionary to Papua, came to the island and spoke to the people about Jesus most of them refused to listen. This story of one man who died for others made no sense to warriors who would kill each other after the smallest insult. But Kone, of all people, was converted. He took his bright-coloured magician's feathers from his hair, and his feathered cloak, and burned them in public. Ceasing to strut about the village as though he owned it, he prayed night and morning for his neighbours to learn to love Jesus, too. But nothing happened, and Kone remained a very lonely Christian.

One day, when Chalmers was away from the village, there was a great tribal feast. The drums beat, the home-made beer flowed freely, excitement rose, and suddenly a quarrel burst out. A tall warrior jumped up, feeling for his spear, his eye on the man who had insulted him. Then, as the spear left the warrior's hand, Kone leapt forward. A moment later he lay on the ground, transfixed and dead.

Kone had shown what it meant to love people enough to die in another man's place.

Rolling Stones

Major Lacoste, a French traveller, was exploring in Afghanistan and the Middle East when he saw the huge boulders near the Kutchan Mountains. They lay in the plain, hundreds of them, dotted over the flat ground near the Caspian Sea. How they had got there he could not imagine, for they were too far from the sea to have been washed inland, and too far from the mountains to have rolled down.

Then, in the distance, he saw that one was moving. Through his binoculars he could clearly see a group of men pushing it. He watched until they stopped pushing, and went on tramping across the plain. In astonishment he turned to one of his servants.

'What is this?' he asked. 'How did these stones get here?'

'In Meshed, in North-east Persia,' said the man, 'there is a mosque which is being built in memory of our saint, Imam Riza. It has a golden dome. But parts of it are not yet finished. It is being built with these stones.'

'But we are hundreds of miles from Meshed!'

'Yes, master,' said the man. 'But every pilgrim on his way to Meshed helps to move them. Some push a little way, some a long way. Some push with their hands or their shoulders. Others carry one in a cart. With everybody pushing, they will all reach Meshed!'

The Steeplejack

It happened in West Bromwich a few years ago.

Two steeplejacks were at work on a factory chimney more than 140 feet above the ground. From the works below the chimney sent up its poisonous fumes of carbonic acid gas. In the street the workers did not notice the change of wind. All they saw was that one of the men had collapsed. The deadly fumes had suddenly been blown downwards on to the platform by the chimney-top.

The other man, panting and sick, tied his mate to a plank to prevent him falling. Then, with his hands clammy, and almost unable to see, he climbed slowly down the long ladder to the ground far below. Looking as though he would collapse, he gasped out the story of what had happened.

At once a man stepped forward. 'What can we do?' he asked.

'We must get him down. If he stays there he'll be killed by the gas.'

'I'll go up and see what I can do.'

The steeplejack seemed to pull himself together suddenly. 'I'd better come and help you. It will need two of us to get him down.'

Together they climbed slowly up the tall chimney. Hours later, so it seemed, they had brought down the sick man. It was only then that the first steeplejack discovered that the rescuer had never climbed higher than the roof of his own house before.

Drawing-room Tale

It was in September 1874. Three sisters, the Misses Pim, had asked a few friends to tea in their Dublin drawing-room to hear a young missionary talk about some of his experiences in India. In particular, he was going to talk about his friends.

His Indian 'friends' were all sufferers from leprosy.

Wellesley Cobb Bailey did not intend to be a missionary. He spent a couple of rough years in the South Seas, returned to Ireland, and then, because he had no idea what to do with himself, went out to India to join his brother who was in the Indian Army. Not that he wanted to join the Army. He thought the Indian Police might be more fun, but, when he was studying the language with a missionary, in order to pass his exams, he suddenly saw quite clearly – so he thought – what God wanted him to do.

He became the headmaster of a missionary school in the Punjab, in North India, at Ambala. When two of his colleagues fell ill he found himself in charge of the whole mission station, which included a tiny home for lepers.

That was the story he told in the drawing-room in Dublin, and very thrilling he made it sound. It was rather more grim when he went on to explain what a dreadful disease leprosy was, and how it robbed people of the use of their hands and feet, so that the only occupation open to them – unless the Church found room for them in a home – was begging.

The Misses Pim promised to try to collect £30 a year to help his work amongst these poor people. To their own astonishment they collected £500 in the first year and £800 in the second. Other leprosy homes besides Bailey's were helped with the money.

That was how there began one of the most wonderful 'missions' in the world – the Mission to Lepers, which is now known as the Leprosy Mission. It works in twenty-four countries and shares in the work of forty-eight missionary societies. Whereas, in those far-off days, leprosy was quite incurable, now we know that it *can* be cured, and *is* being cured. Indeed, someone has said that we could rid the world of leprosy in twenty years if there was enough money and enough skilled workers.

But it all began when three ladies decided to do their little bit of helping.

The Artist

His name was Winston Churchill – *the* Winston Churchill. Everyone has heard of him, all over the world. Thousands of people every year stop at Woodstock, a little town not far from Oxford, to visit his grave in the village churchyard at Bladon. The books he wrote are in the libraries, and his speeches can still be heard on gramophone records.

He was an artist, too. His pictures hung in the Royal Academy, year after year.

But he was very nearly *not* an artist.

You have to imagine him, sitting in front of an easel set up in the countryside. Before him stretched the fields, the trees, in all the gay colours of summer. In one hand he held a brush and in the other a palette of colours. The canvas on the easel was quite clean. There was not even a pencil-mark on it. Churchill sat looking at it. He moved his brush and drew it back again. What if he did something wrong? What if he spoiled the canvas? What if he tried and could not do anything at all . . . if what he put on the canvas just did not make a picture? He nearly put his brush back in the box and folded up the easel.

Then suddenly he dabbed his brush into bright yellow paint, lunged at the easel and made a huge, bright yellow streak across the canvas. It was not the right colour, and it was not in the right place, but he knew that did not matter.

He had begun.

And, once you have begun, you can go on.

The Hunchback

The folk-tale about the hunchback comes from Ireland, and is worth retelling.

Pat was an honest, simple little man and the tragedy of having been born with a humped back had never made him sour or bitter. He had a kind word for boys and girls, a smile for the old people, and he helped anyone he found in need. Perhaps that was why he met the fairy.

She was an Irish fairy, of course, dressed like an old woman. When he saw her gathering peat, Pat bent down to help her – and that was the beginning of his good fortune. When he came back to his lodgings he was carrying a sack of gold.

His greedy landlord determined to find out where it came from, and it did not take long to get the story out of simple Pat. He found out the exact place of the cave the fairy had shown him, and demanded to know whether Pat had really taken everything that was there. Pat shook his head, and admitted that he had not looked. The fairy had said he could have a bag of gold and he took it, without asking for more. Then he remembered something else.

'The fairy *did* say that if anyone tried to find out about it she would make sure they had what I had left behind.'

The greedy landlord laughed and went out of the house. He had not even noticed that Pat was a changed man. It was only when he came out of the cave with two or three pieces of gold in his hand that he found himself bent almost double. Pat had left his humped back behind him in the cave.

Karve's Courage

Women used not to be much respected in India, at any rate for their mental qualities, and when Karve founded the Hindu Women's University in Poona in 1916 there were many people who thought he was out of his mind. Women, they said, could not learn like men – and even if they did they would never have any place in public life. The years have proved how wrong they were. There were others who wondered how Karve had the courage to go on pioneering in such a cause, going on after many defeats in support of women's education. He must have learned courage very early, they said.

He did, indeed.

In 1876 a group of young Hindus determined that they were going to sit for their matriculation examinations. The centre was a town called Satara. They themselves lived at Murad, a 110 miles away. They had little money and, when they set out, had only four days to reach the examination centre. It had never occurred to anyone that they would want to take the exam, anyway.

They began to walk. The first night they slept in a village. The next, they slept under the stars. The third day they managed to get a horse to carry their baggage, but it was so weak that it fell down a gorge, and they spent the night without their baggage in a deep ravine, terrified that they might be attacked by tigers or leopards. The fourth day those who could do so walked another thirty-six miles, and arrived worn out, too tired to take the examination. Except for Karve, that is.

That night Karve set off to walk the 110 miles home again as soon as he could. But he had passed his matriculation.

You Can't Get Away With It

The story about Michael, the seven-year-old who was at home from school with a bad cold, is very old. I am surprised to find it less well known than I had thought.

Michael's mother had to go shopping the second day that he was at home, and she left him indoors with his painting-book, so busy that he hardly had time to look up and say good-bye.

'You're not to go outside this afternoon, Michael.'
He grunted, and went on splashing red paint on the
picture of a fire-engine. 'You understand?' He nodded
this time, and did not answer. He did not need to answer, anyway. He intended to do just that – stay indoors
and get on with his picture.

It was when the water got dirty and he went into
the kitchen to get some more that the trouble started.
Looking out of the window, he saw something going
on in the garden next door. There were lots of people
there, and he could see the ladies' funny hats above
the wall. He wondered what was happening and wished
he could see more. It would not matter if he just ran
out and looked over the wall *very* quickly. There was a
bucket he could stand on just beside the big clump of
red flowers.

A minute later he was standing on it, his head just
above the wall. And right underneath him was a wedding party, the bride in white, the bridegroom with a
grey top-hat, the bridesmaids in yellow dresses . . . and
facing him, a funny photographer who kept popping
his head in and out of a black cloth that covered the
camera.

It was only when he got back into the kitchen that he
wondered what he would say to his mother. He need
not have bothered. She did not even ask if he had been
out of the house.

A week later he found her looking at some lovely
wedding photos which the lady next door had handed
in for her to see. There, under the wall, was the bride,
the bridegroom, the bridesmaids and . . . yes, popping
over the wall was Michael!

Good Master

Velasquez was one of the most famous of all Spanish portrait painters, and when we look at his paintings we know that the praise of his own time was well deserved. Amongst his subjects was the admiral Pareja.

So delighted with his portrait was the admiral that, in reward, he sent the artist a slave with a beautiful gold chain round his neck. Both slave and chain were gifts, and Velasquez named the boy Pareja, in memory of his generous patron. At first the boy was happy enough, for he was given simple work cleaning palettes and brushes, and caring for the canvases in the studio. The artist's pupils, however, tormented him and made fun of him so much that he ran and hid in an attic as often as he could get away. Here he found a way to overcome his misery. On discarded canvases he began to copy his master's work. Gaining courage, he would sometimes work in the studio itself when his master was away from home.

One day a visitor came to the studio before the slave had a chance to hide his work. Worse still, Velasquez himself, whom the boy had thought to be out of the house, walked in to join him. The secret was out. The boy prepared for a beating. To his astonishment, he heard both men describe the painting as a 'work of genius'. Even more to his amazement, he was freed from his slavery and accepted as one of his master's own pupils.

In many a Spanish gallery today can be found the masterpieces of the slave-boy Pareja, alongside those of the great and good master, Velasquez.

Feathers

Don't tell anybody, will you?'

It always began like that. Ellen never meant to tell anybody, either – but if you had heard something about somebody there was not much fun in knowing if you did not share it with someone else. You could always tell *them* not to tell anybody, either. There was no harm in it. But before she left school Ellen was known as 'the girl who could never keep a secret'.

It was the same in her office, and amongst her friends at home. In the end, she began to lose her friends. You could not say *anything* to Ellen if you did not want the whole world to know. The present someone had bought for someone else . . . the quarrel there had been the night before . . . the unkind, and untrue, story she had heard and been asked never to pass on. It was just when she realized that she had hardly any friends left that she came across the story of the woman like herself and how she was cured.

This woman, troubled, like Ellen, because nobody trusted her any more, went to the priest. He told her to kill a fowl and bring him the bag of feathers. She thought it was a stupid cure but did as she was told. For once, she never told anybody about it. Then, taking the bag from her and looking into it to make sure it was full, the priest gave it back.

'Walk home and scatter the feathers as you go! Come back and see me tomorrow night.'

That was even more stupid, thought the woman, but she did as she was ordered and went back the next night.

The priest looked at her solemnly. 'Now, start off for home and collect every one of the feathers you threw away.'

'But . . . But . . .' spluttered the woman, 'how could I? They've blown all over the countryside by now. I could never get them back now. They've gone!'

'Exactly!' said the good priest.

The Muleteers of Ona

The little village of Ona stands not far from Burgos, in Spain. It was famous for nothing at all, but notorious indeed for the temper of its menfolk, most of them mule-drivers. Their work led them up and down the mountain passes, and heat, hard work and natural high tempers led to constant quarrels. Never a man went out without his knife in his belt, and all too often they were drawn in bitter arguments. Many a man went over the precipice, or was left wounded by the roadside, at the end of such quarrels – mostly over things worth no more than a shrug of the shoulders.

At Burgos lived a priest, Father Francis Tarin.

In one place, at least, he knew that the men would be quiet, however angrily they might look at each other. That was in the little church where they worshipped each week. Though they might not follow the service with understanding, they usually listened to what the priest had to say, for he spoke to them as one of themselves.

One Sunday Father Francis preached on charity – a plain talk on love and hate. It must have been even more plain than usual, for at the end of the sermon the priest said that he would spread a blanket before the altar. In it he expected the young men to throw their knives as a sign that they would quarrel no more. Shamefacedly they did so.

That this is no mere legend is proved by the fact that from the knives was cast a great crucifix which stood in Ona for all to see – and remember.

Who's Afraid?

Only when you know that temptation and evil are really big and powerful things can you hope to fight them – and win. It was like that once in the last war. A bundle of papers had arrived from home at a United States Air Force Officers' Mess. It was part of the U.S. Eighth Army Bomber Command, and every man in it knew that he must be ready to play his part in repelling the German aircraft as they attacked Britain. Here and there men flipped over the pages of the glossy magazines, laughing at the jokes, tossing the papers to one another. Suddenly one man rose and walked across to his Commanding Officer with a magazine in his hand.

'What do you think of that, sir?' He pointed to a big, colourful advertisement. The publicity men had twisted an old nursery story into modern words.

'Who's afraid of the new Focke-Wulf?' asked the advert.

The Focke-Wulf was the newest German fighter plane – the newest and best, said the German High Command, which would help them to win the war. The Commanding Officer glanced at the paper and took it away. Shortly afterwards it appeared on the notice-board, with a piece of paper underneath it. The paper was headed – 'Sign Here'.

You might think that it was a joke . . . that nobody would sign it and admit to being afraid. But at the top of the paper was the signature of the Commanding Officer. Before long every combat officer in the Group had added his name.

Those were some of the men who helped to defeat the challenge of German airmen in their new and powerful aircraft. They defeated the Focke-Wulf because they acknowledged it for what it was.

Play to the Whistle!

That is always the rule in football. Play to the whistle. Never argue with the referee. The first thing about playing a game is to know the rules. Or is it?

There is an old tale (with modern China controlled by people who think very little about sport it *must* be old) that the Governor of a Chinese Province wanted all the boys in his provincial schools to learn to play football. He thought it would help them to understand a team spirit, to play fair, to play to the whistle. He sent an instruction to all the Education Officers through the province. 'Every boy in your schools must learn to play football!'

For weeks there was a frantic search for rule-books. When they were found there was a great drive through all the schools to get them learned. 'Goal-posts', 'offside', 'centre-forward', 'wings' were spoken about in places where no one had ever seen a football before. Indeed, they did not all see one then!

'There shall be two teams.'

'Each team shall consist of eleven players.'

'Two goals shall be erected, one at each end of the pitch.'

'The length and breadth of the football pitch shall be . . .'

And so on. And so on.

When the headmaster reported that all his boys knew all about it an inspector came and examined them. They answered all his questions. They recited the rules off by heart, standing in the assembly hall. They had never seen a football, a goalpost or a linesman's flag. But they knew the rules – off by heart.

The inspector was able to make his happy report to the Palace. 'Every boy in this Province can now play football!'

Mikimoto

Mikimoto was ninety-six when he died. Very few people in the West knew his name, and hardly any newspapers wrote much about him when he died. Yet he was one of the most astonishing people in the world. Beginning his working life with no more than a few farthings, he ended his life as a millionaire. But a very special sort of millionaire. He was 'the Pearl King'.

Born in a small village in the centre of the Japanese pearl-fishing area, Mikimoto searched for the perfect pearl. Like many people, he found very few of them. He did learn, however, how pearls were made. A tiny grain of sand would get inside the oyster's shell, making a little wound. The oyster, to protect itself, covered the sand with layer on layer of a special secretion which healed the hurt – and made the pearl. Mikimoto's great discovery was that you could speed up this process. Instead of looking and looking for oysters into which a grain of sand had entered, so that pearls had been formed, why should you not insert the grain of sand right through the shell into the oyster? Then you would not waste time opening thousands of oysters with no pearl inside. You could be *sure* of pearls.

Following his own idea through, he built up an immense industry of 'cultivated' or 'cultured' pearls.

His enemies and rivals attacked him for turning out 'artificial pearls' but he won a big law case in Paris where the pearls were proved to be perfectly genuine. Two things are worth remembering about Mikimoto in which he showed himself greater than the rivals who took him to law. First of all, he refused to put any pearl on the market which he did not consider to be the best he could produce. Then, he refused to lend money to the Japanese Government when it was enlarging its armament industries in preparation for the last war.

When money-grubbing imitators put shabby, poor-grade pearls on the market at cheap prices, he made his protest in his own way. He built a great fire in the streets of Kobe, and shovelled on it 750,000 of his own pearls which he considered too poor to sell and which he was afraid someone else might use when he died.

Only the best was good enough.

The Discontented Quarryman

Possibly, even now, not everyone knows the story of the discontented quarryman. He worked in a lonely place, all by himself. He earned very little money. And he did not like it. Often he would sit down, hot and tired, on a rock and wonder what he would do if he was able to start life all over again.

One day, just as he was splitting a huge piece of rock, he looked up and saw the squire riding by in his carriage. There was a coachman in front, a footman behind, and ahead of him, to make sure the road was clear, rode a groom. As he looked away the quarryman mishit the stone and from his chisel he struck a spark. Then, to his astonishment, from the spark there leapt a fairy.

'What were you wishing just then?' asked the fairy.

The quarryman gaped. 'I wished I was the squire,' he muttered.

And, just as suddenly as the fairy had appeared, he was. With the coachman in front and the footman behind, there he was, riding like the squire, and looking exactly like the squire. What had happened to the real squire nobody knows. But, within a minute or two, he heard a clap of thunder following a flash of lightning, and the rain poured down in torrents. An open carriage had looked wonderful in the sunshine, but now . . .

'An open carriage is no use in the rain,' grumbled the quarryman. 'But I wouldn't mind being that cloud.'

Then, just as suddenly, he was the cloud itself, beating against the mountain.

'I don't like this.' Much better to be the mountain itself, he decided. And, there he was, all at once turned into a mountain. Looking down, he saw a quarryman chiselling away at the rocks, breaking up the mountain stones with his great hammer.

'There'll be nothing of me left soon,' grumbled the mountain. 'I wish I was that quarryman.'

And he was!

The Olive Branch

At Termonde, in Belgium, is the statue of a Jesuit priest, Pierre Jean de Smet. His cloaked figure holds aloft an olive branch. His victory was won, not in Belgium, however, but far away in the United States.

In 1868 a tribal council of the Sioux Indians met

together. The braves wore their war-paint and the great chiefs, Black Moon and Sitting Bull, dominated the council. As they spoke, the warriors grunted angrily. Only one man looked out of place in the fierce assembly – a priest, the only white man amongst them, the only representative of the race the Indians had come to hate and were planning to kill. It was Father Pierre.

For many years these Sioux Indians had fought the advancing Americans, trying to preserve their lands and their hunting-grounds. In their turn, the white men massacred six hundred Sioux, men, women and children. Both nations were weary of the struggle, but neither would trust the other. Now the Indian braves angrily demanded revenge.

'Only one man amongst you has not a forked tongue,' growled Sitting Bull, when the messengers of the American Government had arrived at the Indian village. 'Let him come alone and talk with us. The rest of you go quickly, before we kill you.'

For three days the council went on. For three nights the great chiefs, Sitting Bull and Black Moon, themselves guarded the wigwam where Father Pierre slept peacefully. For three days Father Pierre listened, talked, promised. At the end of those three days, the 'calumet', the pipe of peace, was passed from hand to hand, from Sitting Bull to the priest, from the priest to Black Moon, and through the circle of the braves. Then, at last, Father Pierre went to find the Government's messengers and the pact of peace was signed between the two nations which has never been broken since.

Dearest Possession

Mrs Jeng was a Korean pastor's wife. During the Korean war she lived in a small town which was menaced by the advancing armies from the North and, after a great deal of persuasion, she agreed to seek safety farther away from the battle front, taking her baby with her.

First she escaped to a village on the other side of the bay, but when some of the villagers found her Bible they knew she was a Christian and she was forced to move on. On the mountain roads she saw soldiers in the distance and dropped her Bible down the cliff, so that when she was interrogated the precious book was not found. When the soldiers had gone she climbed down the cliffside to retrieve it.

Later she took refuge in another village. Communist soldiers moved in. Because she was a stranger she was arrested and questioned.

'If she's a Christian, she will have a Bible,' snapped the officer. 'You can always tell Christians. They value their Bibles more than they value their lives!'

The Brave

In the far-off days when the proud Redskins stalked the animals across the wide lands of North America every boy born into the tribe longed for the day when he, too, would be a 'brave' – a trusted warrior who had passed all the rigorous tests which the tribe applied.

He had to be able to track men and animals. He must know the ways of wild beasts and the stars. He needed to shoot his arrows straight at the target, and paddle his canoe safely the through rapids. In addition, he had to pass a final test which was always kept secret by those who had endured it.

One dark night his father would lead him far away from home, into the deep forests. There, with nothing but the stars and the howling animals of the night for company, he had to keep watch until dawn. Nothing could have been more frightening. Other tests he had taken with the boys of his tribe. Now, he was alone. More afraid of the spirits in the darkness than of human enemies, to be by himself, completely, was to be prey to all sorts of fears. Yet to run away would be unthinkable to one who was almost a 'brave'. Almost – but not quite.

Listening for every sound, every movement in the darkness, he watched as the hours went by – every hour seeming as long as the night itself. Then, at last, dawn would break. Looking up, against the red sky he would suddenly see, to his amazement, not the shape of an enemy but the tall, still, silent figure of his father, watching, too. He would know, and remember for ever, that in the loneliest moment of his life he had never really been alone, after all.

The New Sultan

When the old Sultan died, so says the Eastern tale, his son gathered his father's councillors together and asked advice on how to rule his people. Two groups emerged in the council. The first was led by Abu Hassan.

'Your people are rough, harsh and ungrateful,' he asserted. 'You must rule them with a rod of iron, It is the only thing they will understand.'

Ibrahim disagreed. 'They are a kindly and gentle people,' he urged. 'You must rule them with love.'

The young Sultan shrugged his shoulders. 'How do I know which of you is right?' he demanded. 'I will tell you what I will do. You shall both leave the palace for a year. Disguise yourselves. Go out into the market-places and villages. Then come back and tell me what you have found.'

Disguised as pilgrims, the two men went away. At the end of twelve months they came back to make their report. It was what might have been expected. Both were confirmed in their previous opinions, and disagreed just as angrily with each other. Then, stopping the argument, the young king smiled.

'I, too, was in the markets and the villages, but I was also disguised. I watched my people, but I watched you both as well. I found Abu Hassan harsh and angry, and the people answered him with harsh words. Ibrahim I saw treating men gently, and he received nothing but kindness in return.

'I know now whom to trust – and I know how to rule my people!'

All for Revenge

That it happened more than fifty years ago does not really matter. What does matter is that here were two people who really understood what Jesus was talking about when he put into the Lord's Prayer the petitions about forgiveness.

We take them for granted. Those who lived in Jesus's own time must have been completely astonished by them. The great Greek writer, Xenophon, once wrote in praise of one of his heroes: 'No man ever did more good to his friends, and none ever did more harm to his enemies.' A Roman writer kept up his hatred for one of his enemies long after the man was dead by remembering it every time he wrote a letter. 'I write this six hundred and seventy-five days after the death of Clodius', he would begin.

Such men would never have understood the two children of a missionary. In the Boxer Rising in China both the missionary and his wife were brutally murdered – dragged out of their bungalow and massacred with a group of loyal Chinese Christians. Their children, a boy and a girl, watched it happen, though for some reason they themselves were spared. In that terrible moment they vowed revenge.

Back in America the two children grew up, training themselves for the revenge they cherished. At last they were able to return to China. The girl went as a teacher, the boy as a doctor – to pay back the Chinese in the Christian way, forgiving and serving the land where they had suffered so much.

The Caves Under the Earth

'I am the first man to walk along this track for 20,000 years,' thought Norbert Casteret.

The great cave-explorer had been at work in a shaft at Montespan, in France, when he found his progress halted by an ice-cold river. Taking his life into his hands, Casteret plunged into the water, felt along the roof as he kicked his way forwards for two minutes, and then emerged into an immense cavern. It was here that he made one of the greatest discoveries of his life.

On the walls had been carved, with a sharp flint, pictures of animals which ranged Europe thousands of years ago. In another cavern stood sculptures, made by primitive men – a bear, two lions, horses. In the mud, long since turned to stone, were the footprints of the primitive men who once lived here and made these pictures before the empires of Assyria, Babylon or Egypt were founded.

Deep under the earth, too – though not in these long-sealed caves – Casteret found other animals, not carved in stone but alive. There were bats, and tiny crawling insects, hardly living, but still managing somehow to exist. It is hard to understand how they could have survived in the cold, away from the light. But something had happened to these small insects.

The wings they had never used were useless. They crawled because they could no longer fly.

Half and Half

John was seven and his brother Nigel was six. When they were at school, since they were in different classes, they got an quite happily, though they sometimes haggled on the way home. When school was on holiday it was not quite so easy; especially if they both got out of the wrong side of the bed! Usually they had separate beds to get out of, but one day, when Grannie came to stay, both had to use the same double bed in the spare room.

That was the day John hit Nigel with his big sister's hockey stick, and Nigel sat down on John's wonderful castle, which he had built up out of the bricks the builders left behind, and knocked it flat.

Mother heaved a big sigh of relief when they were both safely in bed . . . until Nigel shouted downstairs.

'John's being horrid. He wants half the bed.'

'That's quite right, Nigel. You must have half each.'

'Yes, Mummy,' roared Nigel. 'But John wants his half in the middle!'

(2) For Older People
and Boys and Girls, too

Do-Gooder

> She was a 'sunbeam',
>   So happy and bright,
> Shedding good cheer
>   To left and to right;
> Doing her bit
>   With zeal unabated;
> She was a 'sunbeam'
>   – And, boy, was she hated!

'From Greenland's Icy Mountains'

I would never choose – or sing – the Victorian's most famous missionary hymn. It breathes the patronage and ignorance about other men's faiths of an age that, I hope, is dead. But for Reginald Heber, the writer of the hymn, I have nothing but humble affection. That he was a man of his time, with the Victorian's attitudes is perfectly natural. But he was far more than this – and he had much to teach us. On his memorial in St Paul's Cathedral is an indication that, in spirit, he was far ahead of most of us.

For two years after leaving Oxford he travelled in Germany and Russia and was then appointed to an

English living before responding to a suggestion that he should go to India as Bishop of Calcutta. The title meant little. He was 'in charge' not only of Calcutta but of the missionary work in the whole of India and Ceylon. Even more astonishing, his diocese stretched to Australia!

At the age of forty-three he died.

In his years in India, Bishop Heber had grown to love the Indian people, and to understand their need of Christ. He offered his own faith despite 'Greenland's icy mountains' – without trying to belittle their own. It is fitting that, on his memorial in St Paul's, two words which seldom go together should be used to describe him.

He was, it says, a man of 'intense zeal and toleration'.

The Millionaire's Creed

What does a millionaire believe in? Himself? Money? Power? A millionaire once broadcast to the nation the creed he held.

'I believe in the dignity of labour, whether with head or hand; that the world owes no man a living, but that it owes man an opportunity to make a living.

'I believe in the sacredness of a promise, that a man's word should be as good as his bond; that character – not wealth or power or position – is of supreme worth.

'I believe that every right implies a responsibility; every opportunity an obligation; every possession a duty.

'I believe in an all-wise and all-loving God, named by whatever name; and that the individual's highest fulfilment, greatest happiness, and widest usefulness are to be found in living in harmony with his will.

'I believe that love is the greatest thing in the world; that it alone can overcome hate; that right can and will triumph over wrong.'

The millionaire was John D. Rockefeller.

But the creed is good for Everyman.

Memorial of Infamy

Visiting the Doge's Palace in Venice I found myself glad that my failures were kept in my own heart.

Amongst the memorials to the great rulers of the sea-state there are empty spaces. Under the arches of the palace are other memorial tablets. To the visitor they look like 'more obituary notices'. To those with some Italian, who stop to read carefully, they are reminders of infamy.

Here is a tablet to Girolamo Loredan and Giovanni Contarini. It proclaims that they were banished from the state because, to the grave danger of the city and of Christendom, they surrendered the fortress to the Turks.

And another, to Pietro Bonito, a mere clerk in the Armaments Office. He is to be remembered as long as men live or the tablet remains, as a man who mismanaged and embezzled the funds committed to his care.

As I looked, I hoped that God has not as long a memory as men.

'Standing in the Need of Prayer'

A Member of Parliament, lecturing to his constituents

about the way in which the country is governed and about the procedures of Parliament, said he would begin with the opening of the day's work in the House of Commons.

'The Chaplain gets up,' he said, 'looks round the House and prays for the country!'

Baalbeck

Baalbeck is an oasis set in the grey-brown desert, but it is also a place which takes the traveller back through the ages to the long-ago glories of the Phoenician civilization. Here, more than two thousand years ago, there was a great Phoenician town. When the Greeks came to Syria they built their own lovely temples over the ruined city. Then came the Romans, and the city lying ruined under the scorching Middle Eastern sun is largely their creation. Some of the pillars and halls were set up on immense granite blocks – ten feet thick, twelve feet wide. They must each weight not less than a thousand tons.

Sir Leonard Woolley, the archaeologist, was once exploring the site in company with a Palestinian overseer. Woolley noticed the design, the carvings, the sign which dated each separate ruin. An artist might have seen quite different things. A tourist – and tourists now have Baalbeck on their itineraries – would perhaps have gazed open-mouthed that the 'ancients' could have done such work. It was the overseer, however, who seemed to have got to the heart of the matter. He was not concerned with architects or artistry.

'What a foreman they must have had,' he said, shaking his head in wonder; 'what a foreman!'

The Sundial

Henry van Dyke, who wrote a famous Christmas book, *The Story of the Other Wise Man*, and an excellent hymn, *They who tread the path of labour follow where My feet have trod*, also wrote this little verse about a sundial.

> *The shadow by my finger cast*
> *Divides the future from the past;*
> *Before it, sleeps the unknown hour*
> *In darkness and before thy power;*
> *Behind its unrelenting line*
> *The vanished hour, no longer thine;*
> *One hour alone is in thy hands,*
> *The 'now' on which the shadow stands.*

The Reredos

Our forefathers were great craftsmen, and they loved nothing better than to decorate their churches with sculptures on which they lavished all their skill. The frontages of our great cathedrals, the pew-ends, even the miserere-seats which were seldom likely to be noticed, were decorated – the latter sometimes rather maliciously – with saints, emblems and, from to time, the features of real people.

The same skills are still offered to God in many of our churches. One of these churches is at Bingham, in Nottinghamshire. Dedicated to All Saints, it is not surprising that the reredos is carved with many saints who might well be remembered. There is St Hugh, the great bishop who built Lincoln Cathedral to the glory of God and was himself a lover of common people. There is St Wilfrid of York – architect and autocrat.

There is another figure, too – without a name. A

reminder that ordinary people are 'called to be saints'. It is just a charming carving of a woman at her wash-tub.

Rope Across Niagara

Everyone knows the name, Niagara. Not so many, today, remember the name of Blondin.

Blondin was one of the great high-wire walkers of all time. In the days before shrewd business-men set out to make fortunes by exploiting the immense cataract a huge crowd gathered at the Falls to see Blondin undertake a feat that might very likely end in his death. A wire had been slung across the Falls and Blondin was to attempt to walk it.

He moved on to the slim cable, balanced carefully and began to edge his way along. Almost without breathing the crowd waited for tragedy – but Blondin moved slowly and securely to the opposite side. The crowd gained its breath again, and cheered.

That was not the end. The high-wire man took a wheelbarrow and, just as carefully as he had gone across, wheeled the barrow back across the wire. This time the cheer was louder than ever.

'Did you think I could do it?'

The murmur was hesitant.

'Do you think I can do it again?'

This time there was no doubt. He could do it again and again.

The acrobat turned to the people nearest to him saying: 'Will one of you gentlemen sit in the barrow while I wheel it across?'

That was another matter. There were no volunteers.

I Believe

Dr John Paton, the pioneer missionary to the New Hebrides in the South Seas, lived a life of courage, adventure and achievement which witnessed to the power of the God in whom he believed. But when it came to translating the word 'believe' into the language of the people to whom he ministered, that was a more difficult matter. For him one of the key-texts of the Bible was John 3: 16. But how do you render 'whosoever believeth' into a tongue where the word does not exist at all?

He had been praying that God would give him some clue to the problem when one of his servants came into the house after a long, hard day's work. 'I am so weary,' he said, 'that I must lean my whole weight on the chair.'

In that moment Paton knew what phrase he must use to translate the word 'believe'.

The Cathedral

They had almost finished their continental holiday – the first time they had been out of England. Everything was new to them, and almost everything had been wonderful. Now, amongst the gay and friendly pavement cafés, they were sitting in the shadow of a great cathedral, the last stop of the last coach-outing.

A Frenchman sat down beside them and began to talk – fortunately, in English. They told him happily about their holiday and the things they had seen. Finally, because it was the last thing they had seen, they enthused about the cathedral.

He nodded, pleased with their praise.

'Yes,' he said, 'it is good. But your Westminster Abbey! Ah – that is *magnifique*!'

'I suppose so,' responded the girl. 'But, to tell you the truth, I've never been iside it.'

The Frenchman looked shocked. 'No? But where do you live?'

'London,' she replied.

Palace of the Five Winds

Every tourist in India knows of Agra, and has stood in the moonlight to admire the Taj Mahal. Not so many know the rose-red city of Fatehpur Sikri, twenty miles away. Fatehpur Sikri is dead . . . dead for centuries. Its creator, the Emperor Akbar, deserted it twenty years after it was built, for some reason that nobody knows.

The guide took us round the huge ruins, with little but ghosts and a few peasants for company. The breeze blew gently through the Council Chamber and the Mint. A rat ran across the floor of the elephant stables. Our eyes were dazzled by the gleam of the sun on deep red sandstone and we stopped by the great courtyard, with its black and white square of marble, where the emperor and his courtiers played chess with slave-girls for pieces.

From the Palace of the Five Winds we looked across to the balcony where the Emperor Akbar, in the days of our own Elizabeth the First, would sit crosslegged, just after dawn, to hear the complaints and requests of his subjects.

The guide whispered by our side, his voice muted to the silent city. 'See! At that place, every morning, every subject in the realm had access to the king.

There was no difference then in their rank or position. Many came just because it was good to begin the day in the king's presence!'

The Barrel

The cooper was a miserly man who lived and worked for himself. One day there came an old, bent beggar who asked him for a drink of water. The cooper refused. He was too busy.

'There's a fountain in the square,' he shouted. 'Go and get a drink from there, if you want one.'

The old man said nothing. He tottered away without looking back. In a few minutes the cooper had finished his task and set off to test the bowl at the fountain. As he turned the corner he saw his visitor lying on the ground, almost fainting.

'Water!' he called.

The cooper hardly stopped to look at him. If he had gone straight to the fountain he would have had his drink. That was what came of interrupting busy people at their work. He trundled his new barrel on to the fountain and put it underneath the running water. Then he watched, incredulous. The water ran into the barrel, but it would not fill. He pulled it out, looked at the staves, searched for a hole. There were no faults. He thrust it back and swore. The barrel refused to fill.

A crowd gathered, hardly believing their eyes. Then, at last, in the crowd, he saw a small boy escorting the fainting man to the fountain. Almost unbidden, the cooper felt a sense of shame. How could a man live without water?

A tear dropped from his eye into the barrel.

Then, at last, the barrel began to fill.

Private Paper

She was over ninety when she died, a charming, gay old lady who chose to walk rather than ride to church, and she maintained her interest – it was never curiosity – in the friends, old and young, whom she had known and loved.

'How does she keep so bright?' people asked, in wonder and affection.

The answer was found in a set of verses, copied out in her own handwriting, amongst her private papers. Nothing could have been more true of her than this – a group of verses which said nothing about God. She, too, seldom spoke of her faith. Yet her life, like these lines, implied a faith that was deep and purposeful.

> *It's the way you live, not the way you talk,*
> *Not the way you preach, but the way you walk,*
> *That the world will judge, whatever you claim,*
> *That the world will praise, or the world will blame.*
>
> *It's the way you do, not the things you say,*
> *Not the way you spend but the way you pay,*
> *It will like the least, or like the most.*
> *It's the way you work, not the way you boast.*
>
> *It's the way you sing, not the way you sigh,*
> *Not the way you whine but the way you try,*
> *That will hold you down, or will help you far;*
> *Not the way you seem, but the way you are.*

Tschiffely's Ride

Tschiffely's Ride was a best-seller in its time – a notable account of a daring feat. A. F. Tschiffely set out to ride from Argentina to Washington, a distance of about 10,000 miles through unfamiliar and some-times unexplored country. Primitive Indians, despised by white people, were his most constant companions. It was in a Central American Indian village that he was nearly arrested.

During his first day in the village he noticed a swarthy policeman walking suspiciously behind him wherever he went. At first he took little notice until he saw that the man kept taking a piece of paper from his pocket and studying it. Finally Tschiffely went to the police-station to ask what he was supposed to have done. The inspector summoned his constable and they fell into a long conversation. The policeman laid the paper on the table – a notice about a Swedish cashier who had absconded with a large share of the bank's proceeds. The inspector laughed, clapped the con-stable on the back and pushed him towards the door.

As he went out he turned and pointed to Tschiffely. 'Well,' he argued, 'he's a white man – and all white men look the same, anyway!'

Useless!

Dictionaries are more interesting than they sometimes appear. An American dictionary printed in 1901 has this definition.

'*Uranium*: a worthless white metal; not found in the United States.'

Three Angry Women

It is rather terrible how wrongly you can judge people out of sheer ignorance. Like the three women who were holiday-making in Bulgaria. Behind the Iron Curtain now, it was just as inaccessible in the 1930s when they visited it. In the mountains were brigands and through-out the country desperate poverty. Even to find shelter from the rain was difficult, especially when it came on with the blinding suddenness of this torrent.

Ahead of them they saw a cottage, and knocked at the door. A peasant woman opened it and stared at them. In sign-language they pointed out that they would like shelter. The woman stepped back, shaking her head vigorously. Angrily they explained – a few minutes shelter would cost her nothing. The woman still shook her head. With no knowledge of the language they talked more loudly, as though that would make her understand. Frustrated, they stood in the rain until the woman put out her hand and drew them inside.

They assumed that something had made her change her inhospitable ways until they discovered, days later, that the village people of Bulgaria shook their heads from side to side instead of nodding when they meant 'Yes . . . of course!'

Kind Thought

I'll be kind to all dumb animals
And give small birds a crumb;
I'll be kind to human beings, too,
– They're often pretty dumb.

The Fire

John was no stranger to Africa. He had lived and worked there all his life, most of it amongst village people. He understood their ways and was permitted to share in their life, even though he was an outsider and represented 'law and order'.

He had many memories to cherish. One moment, so he said, remained in his mind above all others.

He was sitting outside the hut which had been given to him as a 'safari house'. The moon was high in the sky and his fire burned brightly. Round the circle of beehive huts the men sat round their fires, talking in low, easy tones. Then, suddenly, he was aware of a woman standing beside him, holding a charred stick in her hand.

'Our fire has gone out,' she said, quietly. 'May I light my stick from your fire?'

Once Upon a Time

I know that when I copied it out from 'somewhere' I thought of the way in which, in our age, professional women are coming into their own. But I thought, too, of one woman who wanted to be a doctor and another who longed to be a politician . . . long-ago dreams they admit only to their friends. They have ended up as 'just mothers'. But, though their dreams come back sometimes and can never be fulfilled, they are good mothers.

> Once upon a time, I planned to be
> An artist of celebrity.
> A song I thought I'd write one day,
> And all the world would homage pay.
> I longed to write a famous book.
> But, what I really did was – cook.
> My life with simple tasks is filled
> And I have not done what I willed –
> Yet, when I see boys' hungry eyes,
> Thank God I make good apple pies.

Hell

'Some people say there's no such place as hell,' said the architect, 'but they're wrong. There is. I've been there.'

The conversation followed a sermon on the life hereafter, and the minister raised his eyebrows. 'A tragedy, perhaps?'

'Not really. I slipped into hell on a Friday night. It was like this. I was a young man then, and there were two of us in the drawing office. We shared a large table, and one Friday morning we had an argument. It doesn't matter what it was about. I was in the wrong, anyway. We both went out to lunch without speaking to one another. When we came back we were both so angry and embarrassed that we didn't speak to each other the whole afternoon. At five o'clock we both went home without even a civil good-night.

'On the Monday morning I got to the office early so that I wouldn't have to say "Good-morning" to the other chap when he walked in. But he'd had the same idea, and was earlier than I was! So neither of us spoke.

'After that, there wasn't anything to do but keep silent. It isn't easy when you can't even ask for a rubber or a ruler, or say "thank you" when one was passed to you.

'It went on like that through Monday and Tueday. Wednesday morning was the same. I knew what Hell was, then – it wasn't a place . . . just a state of mind . . . a state of separation.

'I got out of it on Wednesday afternoon . . . when I apologized.'

Last Grasp

Catterick Camp has been, for very many years, the

home of the 'Signals'. There hung there a picture which no member of the Royal Corps of Signals was ever likely to forget.

When signals used to be sent by wire there was always the danger that a shell, or an enemy patrol, might cut the wire, and it was the unenviable task of the signal-man to crawl out, often under sniping or bombardment, to repair the line.

The picture, dating from the First World War, shows a signalman who has been sent out to do this task. It is clear what has happened. When he has just begun his job a sniper's bullet has killed him. He lies dead on the ground. Dead – but not a failure.

In his last moment he has grasped the broken wires, one in each hand. The circuit is complete. Dead he may be, but the connection has been made.

Under the picture there is a one-word title: 'Through.'

Where the Bible Ends

It was Dr T. R. Glover, the Cambridge orator whose religious books were best-sellers, who told the story of Elizabeth.

She was lying on the mat in front of the fire, turning over a Bible – a very different book from her own big 'picture book of Bible stories'. Suddenly she looked up.

'Barbara,' she said to her bigger sister, who was sitting knitting. 'Did you know that the Bible begins with Genesis and ends in Revolutions?'

The Music Makers

It must be wonderful to be famous . . . to hold people

in your grasp as you play or sing to them . . . to travel the world.

The concert musicians would not disagree. But they know the cost, too. Never has there been a more popular or beloved concert violinist than Fritz Kreisler. 'I have visited almost every town in the world with a population of over 100,000 people', Kreisler once wrote. 'And of them all I know only the railway station, the hotel and the concert hall.'

Marion Anderson, the great prima donna, said this: 'All my life I have thought and dreamed of nothing but music, and worked for nothing else. Now I find what it costs. It is always a question of travel. I arrive at a town. I go to a hotel. I sleep. I go to a concert. I leave, and catch the train, the boat or the plane. One's life is never one's own.'

Fame costs more than we sometimes realize.

In Chester Cathedral

Who wrote it I do not know. I found it in a book, its author anonymous. Its title announced that it was 'Found in Chester Cathedral', but whether in the visitors' book or on the floor it did not state.

> *Give me a good digestion, Lord,*
> *And also something to digest;*
> *Give me a healthy body, Lord,*
> *With sense to keep it at its best.*
> *Give me a healthy mind, good Lord,*
> *To keep the pure and good in sight,*
> *Which, seeing sin, is not appalled*
> *But finds a way to set it right.*
> *Give me a mind which is not bored,*
> *That does not whimper, whine or sigh;*

Don't let me worry overmuch
About the fussy thing called 'I'.
Give me a sense of humour, Lord,
Give me the grace to see a joke,
To get some happiness from life
And pass it on to other folk.

'Sign, Please!'

There were many things which the vicar liked about his new parish – and one which he soon got to dislike intensely.

It was not in the drab part of the town, as his previous church had been. The music was good, the congregations reasonable. There were few anxieties about money, either for the church or the congregation, in this well-placed suburban area. The people were charming – until he found the black spot.

Within the first month the organist's wife had told him some unhappy things about the churchwarden's older daughter. A pleasant tea-party included a group who shared their knowledge of some of the other church members – who were not there.

At the end of a month he preached a sermon about the evils of gossip. Everyone agreed that it was just what was wanted – for somebody else. They even told him who should have been listening most carefully.

That was when he decided on somewhat more positive action.

The next time a caller slipped into a rather sordid little tale he sat behind his desk, making notes on a pad. She went on to talk of other things but, as she rose to leave, he stopped her and read over the notes he had put down. 'That *was* what you said?' he asked. The visitor nodded a little reluctantly.

'Will you sign your name at the bottom, please?' he asked.

Slowly the gossip stopped.

The Golfer and the Gate

Lloyd George once told the story of the village doctor whom he knew in his youth.

The doctor was a golfer, a kind and gentle man who was loved and trusted by all his patients. He had time for their personal anxieties as well as their physical illnesses – and this was all the more surprising since he had had so many troubles of his own. There were those who wondered that he was not impatient with other people as well as nerve-racked by his personal anxieties.

It was after they had been playing golf that the politician gained the clue to the situation. They were walking back across the fields from the course and Lloyd George, giving precedence to the older man, came out of a field behind him. The doctor turned and saw that he had left the gate open. Nothing could be a worse fault in farming country. The doctor turned back, closed the gate, and caught up with the young man. He only spoke one sentence, as they walked on, before resuming their interrupted conversation, but it illuminated his whole philosophy.

'I have gone through life shutting the gate on what I have left behind,' he said.

The Tramp

In her *Autobiography* Margot Asquith has a childhood

story from her early days in Scotland. She had slipped out from home and wandered along the road until she saw an old and very dirty tramp sitting on a bank of heather. She began, with customary forthrightness, questioning him about his life. What was his name? What did he do? Where had he come from? The man was content, without visions and ambition.

'But how do you make up your mind where you'll go next?' Margot demanded.

'Och, that's easy. I simply see which way the wind's blowing and put me back to it!'

Goodbye

The story of Rupert Brooke's goodbye used to be better known than it now is. Seemingly sentimental, there are many people who would understand it, out of their own experience.

In the preface to his poems is told the story of how the young, First World War poet left Liverpool. There was no one at the landing-stage to see him off, though most other soldiers seemed to have girl-friends or relatives in plenty. Looking round, he saw a small boy.

'What's your name?' he asked.

'William.'

'Would you like to earn sixpence, William?'

The boy's eyes gleamed. Sixpence was a lot of money in those far-away days.

'Here it is.' He passed it over, bright and gleaming. 'All you've got to do is stand on the landing-stage and wave your handkerchief as the ship goes out? Will you do that?'

As the troopship pulled away from the quay the

poet stood by the rail waving to a small boy, who may never have been lonely in his life, but who was waving his handkerchief to a man he probably thought was slightly mad.

Three Wishes

I wish I were beneath a tree,
Just sleeping in the shade,
With all the bills I've got to pay
Paid!

I wish I were beside the sea,
Or sailing in a boat,
With all the things I've got to write
Wrote!

I wish I were on that high hill
And sleeping in the sun
With all the things I've got to do
Done!

Successful Man

Oswaldo de Teixiera stood by the immense window, looking out across the splendid bay, famous amongst the splendid views of South America. Dark-haired, dark-skinned, with capable hands and a sensitive face, he wore clothes which proclaimed that they came from good tailors, just as the furniture and possessions in the room itself were echoes of riches. They marked him a successful man. As, indeed, he was.

Teixiera was born poor. He knew nothing of his father, and his mother worked hard to support them both. Young Oswaldo early showed a talent for drawing, and he practised it in the only way possible – he became a pavement artist in the fabulous resort of Copacobana, the playground of South American millionaires.

It was on the pavement, one day, that a professor from the art school noticed him. From that day, his life changed.

From the art school he travelled to Italy, and in Florence his genius blossomed fully at last. Years later he returned to America and became known as the greatest artist in the southern continent. He was more influential than the professor who had befriended him, and just as generous.

Yet, turning back from the window, Teixiera looked seriously at his friend. 'Success is the dullest thing in the world,' he said. 'It is the struggle to succeed that makes life worthwhile.'

Holiday Story

They met on the train on the Monday morning.

'Been on holiday yet?' asked Smith.

'Yes,' said Brown, glumly. 'Rotten time, though. And you?'

'Yes. Just come back. We managed quite nicely though. Had a nice fortnight.'

'Lucky for you. We got back on Saturday, too. But it rained half the time we were away.'

'Oh, we were lucky,' said Smith. 'Where did you go?'

'St Ives.'

'Oh, how odd. So did we. And it was fine half the time we were there.'

Market Day

Mark Guy Pearse was one of Methodism's most famous preachers. A Cornishman, from the days long before coaches and cars turned the narrow lanes of the Duchy into highways, he drew many of his illustrations from the simple ways of ordinary people.

There was the story of the old woman going home from market who was offered a lift in his gig by a passing farmer.

First she pushed up her heavy basket and then climbed laboriously into the trap. After half a mile the farmer looked at her, basket on her lap and her arms filled with packages.

'Put your basket down, me dear,' he counselled her. 'If the old mare can carry you she can carry your burden, too.'

You can imagine what use the preacher made of such a tale.

God, the Gardener

He was not a busybody; just a good neighbour – the sort of man who naturally talked to anybody whom he passed on the road or saw at work in a garden. Being retired, there were plenty of other things to do at home. Perhaps that is why he went out. Perhaps, too, it was why he talked when he got out. He was also a good man who never lost an opportunity for a word of 'witness'.

Walking down a road he seldom used he noticed that a house which had been up for sale for months had changed hands. Indeed, the new tenant must have been there for some time, judging by the garden. The lawn was trimmed, the roses were pruned, and the rockery was planted.

'You're doing a nice job there,' he said, leaning on his walking-stick. 'You and God together, that is.'

The gardener looked up, red-faced and a little out of breath from his digging.

'Aye? Well, you should have seen it when God had it to himself!' he commented, caustically.

An Igbo Poem

Harcourt White was a patient at the Uzuakoli Leprosy Settlement, a poet and musician whose works have been made known in Britain by my colleague, Dr Frank Davey, who spent over twenty years of his medical ministry at Uzuakoli.

In an age when we speak glibly of 'depth' there is nothing glib about this lovely poem.

Jesus, my Lord, you are depth,
   Indeed, my Lord, you are depth:
Having no sin, yielding to no evil
   Your hands sweet and clean,
Yet you became the Friend of sinners,
   Your love freely shared among them.
Jesus, my Lord, you are depth,
   Indeed, my Lord, you are depth:
For though you fed crowds upon crowds
   Until they had enough and to spare,
Yet you yourself suffered the pangs of hunger
   For forty days in the wilderness.
Jesus, my Lord, you are depth,
   Indeed, my Lord, you are depth:
Loosing the chains of those who were bound
   In body or in spirit,

Yet you yourself, in chains went the dolorous way
  From Gethsemane to Calvary.
Jesus, my Lord, you are depth,
  Indeed, my Lord, you are depth:
For though you are God, the King of Heaven,
  Creator of earth and Heaven,
Yet you left the joy of Heaven and became man,
  That you may save man.

The Advocate

In the Katanga country of the Congo a missionary was trying to translate the Bible into the language of the people. It was a hard task when most of the people had few words and a limited experience of life beyond their own villages.

Amongst these people the chief counted for a very great deal. Much of his time was given to settling disputes and administering justice. People came to him all day long, where he sat before his hut on his 'stool'. Often the missionary sat nearby, learning and listening.

Beside the chief there was always an elder who was addressed as 'Nsenga'. A stranger might have thought it was his name, but it was not. It was his title. His task was not so much to give advice as to stand beside those who came to the court and, if necessary, to put the very words into their mouths.

One day, as he watched and listened to 'Nsenga', the missionary knew he had found the exact word for a New Testament one which had baffled him. He had found the translation for the 'advocate', the Holy Spirit.

The Lucky Young Man

There cannot be many people who have not imagined what it would be like to inherit a fortune. There are even some people who have whiled away happy hours planning how they would spend it if they did.

George Whitefield, the colleague of John Wesley's early days, knew one such lucky young man.

In Gloucester, his home town, he found him one morning in the congregation – a pleasant youth whose uncle had just died and left him all his money. Whitefield was not unaccustomed to praying for the poor, but the prayers that day included this petition: 'The prayers of this congregation are asked for a young man who has recently fallen heir to a large fortune.'

Waterfront

Waterfront is an American novel which deals with the racketeers. A longshoreman is murdered in New York City by a gang of thugs. There are corrupt politicians who refuse to act, and decent citizens who are afraid to interfere. In the end it is an unexpected man who sets out to bring the murderers to justice. A local priest organizes the longshoremen into a fighting unit and, at the risk of his own life, puts an end to the racketeers.

Why should a priest concern himself with such things, when his task is dealing with men's souls?

The answer is supplied by the dead man's sister.

The priest had gone to comfort the relatives. 'I'll be in the church if you need me,' he assured them as he left the tenement.

The murdered man's sister turned on him angrily.

'Was there ever a saint who hid himself in the church?' she demanded, furiously.

Those were the words which turned him into a man who really cared.

The Heroes

He died – a hero in the fight –
And so they crowned his name with light.
She lived for many a tortured year;
They only said, 'She's getting queer'.

Gettysburg

It is said that any high school student is so proud of being an American that he knows Lincoln's speech at Gettysburg by heart. There is on record an account of a high-school speech day in which one senior recited the speech word perfect, and, with the seeming authority of Lincoln himself. Afterwards, however, an old man came up to him.

'Son,' he said, 'I liked the way you gave that speech, but you make the same mistake as everyone else. You said, "the government *of* the people, *by* the people, *for* the people". But that wasn't what Mr Lincoln said, son. I heard him, and I know. Mr Lincoln wasn't thinking of prepositions. He was thinking of people.

'He said: "Of the *people*, by the *people*, for the *people*." '

Bridge of Shrines

On a continental holiday you may come across many things worth noting – but it will always pay you to note down the name of the place you find them. When I came across the bridge of shrines I forgot – the memory remains very vividly, but not the town!

In many ways the bridge was ordinary enough, though the shrines, fairly common on roads and bridges, were far from ordinary. Each was a figure of Christ – and each was differently dressed. In one the Lord was dressed as a shepherd; in another as a shoemaker; in others as a baker and a blacksmith. If *we* stopped to look there is no doubt that other people paused long ago, too. They might stare with interest at them all, but I can imagine that when they came to the figure in which Christ bore the implements of their own trade, they stopped not only to look, but to pray.

Editorial

This Editorial appeared in an American magazine.

'It is a gloomy moment in history. Not for many years – not in the lifetime of most men who read this – has there been so much grave and deep apprehension. Never has the future seemed so incalculable as at this time. In our own country, there is universal unrest and millions of our fellow-citizens are fearful of the future.

'In Europe and Asia the political cauldron seethes and bubbles with uncertainty. Russia hangs like a cloud, dark and silent, upon the horizon, while the energies of the British . . . are sorely tried, and are yet to be tried more sorely, in coping with vast and deadly disturbed relations in India and China.

'Of our own troubles no man can see the end. They are, as yet, fortunately, mainly political and industrial, . . . we must resist and subdue the forces which are the occasion of this widespread evil and harmful distress.'

It is an Editorial which might almost have been written today.

But it appeared in *Harper's Weekly* – in October, 1857.

The Frog

The only reason I have included this bit of nonsense is because I like it – not because it will do anybody any good.

> *What a wonderful bird de frog are –*
> *When he stand he sit almost;*
> *When he hop he fly almost;*
> *He ain't got no sense hardly;*
> *He ain't got no tail neither;*
> *And when he sit*
> *He sit on what he ain't got almost.*